THE BUILD-A-HABIT GUIDE
A Research-Backed Program for Making Habits Stick

A 10-week guided program designed by a behavioral
scientist to help you master habit formation.

(THIS BOOK BELONGS TO)

(IF FOUND, PLEASE RETURN TO)

LEARN MORE
www.therapynotebooks.com

THERAPY NOTEBOOKS
Published by Subject Matters

ISBN: 9781735084657
Printed in the United States of America

LEAD BEHAVIORAL SCIENTIST
Asaf Mazar, PhD

EDITED BY
Diana Hu, PsyD
Axel Valle, PsyD
Meghan Nesmith
Gina Ryder

DESIGNED BY
Monumento.Co

BRANDING BY
High Tide

IF YOU ARE IN URGENT NEED
OF MEDICAL ASSISTANCE:
Dial 9-1-1

FOR IMMEDIATE MENTAL HEALTH
CRISIS SUPPORT:
Dial 9-8-8

SAMHSA National Helpline
1-800-622-HELP (4357)

Crisis Text Line
Text HOME to 741741

How This Book Helps You

1   Learn the practical science of habit formation.

     Instead of reading about habits (and you may have already
     read an article or book—or two!), we help you put the theory
     to practice. You'll learn about the science of habits, and you'll
     also learn easy-to-use habit-building tools that you can apply
     to any habit you want to form.

2   Develop one simple habit that sticks.

     If you've tried forming a new habit before, you know how
     challenging it can be. We help you hone in on a habit and
     build it from beginning to end.

3   Have fun and use your intuition.

     You learn best when you're having fun. We designed *The Build-
     a-Habit Guide* to be playful and intuitive. You'll get to engage your
     creativity and problem-solving skills to bring your habit to life.

4   Discover what works for you by tracking your progress and
     having a space to reflect.

     Popular habit programs will try to sell us a single "silver bullet"
     that will magically make our habits fall into place. When things
     inevitably don't go as planned with a special panacea, it's easy to
     feel discouraged or disillusioned. Take heart in the reality that
     building a habit is not a one-size-fits-all model; it's an iterative,
     individual process that requires experimentation. To discover
     what's working and what's not, you'll track your progress in a
     guided, structured space where you can test and learn what sticks.

5   Lean on experts to provide you with research-backed principles
     and practical wisdom.

     We worked with experts who extensively research the field of
     behavioral psychology and help clients improve their lives. You'll
     receive compassionate guidance, step-by-step instruction, and
     thoughtful prompts to make small changes for a meaningful
     impact in your life.

Foreword

"Every good that is worth possessing must be paid for
in strokes of daily effort."

—William James,
American Psychologist and Philosopher

In our work creating rigorously researched, empathetic, and
accessible notebooks for mental health, we've worked with over
a hundred clinical psychologists and licensed therapists. Time and
time again, they've told us: one of the foundations of healing—of
truly flourishing—is a consistent daily routine that prioritizes
self-care.

Building and maintaining a consistent daily routine is,
of course, easier said than done.

In our busy world, we all know that it can feel simpler and
safer to stay the same. How do you bring yourself to step out of
your comfort zone when change feels so hard? So we started with
this question: how can we empower people to change behavior
for the better—and how can we make that process a little easier
and a lot more engaging?

That's how *The Build-a-Habit Guide* was born.

We partnered with a habit scientist and experienced
clinicians to create this practical, creative, and scientifically
sound guide to help you learn how to build habits with staying
power. *The Build-a-Habit Guide* was shaped by the understanding
that behavior change is not one-size-fits-all, and that truly
meaningful progress involves room to make mistakes, and a

willingness to discover what works for you. The experience you're about to embark on is the first of its kind and is backed by cutting-edge research. By the time you complete the guide, you'll have developed skills to reliably build consequential habits for life.

We know that implementing one new habit is not a cure-all, and the journey to change can be bumpy. But we also know this is one meaningful step in the right direction; and through this process, you'll gain the skills to continue building a life grounded in your personal values—a life that supports who you want to be, and how you want to live.

Scan the QR code to meet our experts

The How-To Guide

This book is a 10-week guided program to help you build one simple habit. We centered this program on the idea that successful habit formation is based on playful experimentation to figure out what approach works best for you. This How-To Guide breaks down the main parts of the book so you're prepared for what's next.

PHASE	SECTION	DESCRIPTION
Phase I: Lay the foundation of strong habit formation.	Introduction	An overview of the book and what to expect for the next ten weeks
	Understanding Habits	A primer on how habits are formed and the key concepts to keep in mind
	Choose Your Habit	An exercise to select a habit that is simple and helpful for you
	Create Your Habit Plan	An exercise to create your first Habit Plan
Phase II: Discover what works for you by experimenting with your Habit Plan.	Repeat and Refine (Week I - IV)	Four weeks of daily check-ins and weekly reflections to identify what cues work best for you
Phase III: Maintain your progress through consistency.	Daily Tracking Entries (Week V - X)	Six weeks to continue your progress through additional tracking entries

Contents

Welcome to the Guide

We hope this experience is fun and fulfilling for you. Before you get started on your habit formation journey, let's warm up by setting your intentions.

What brings you to *The Build-a-Habit Guide*? Maybe you want to build a specific habit, learn the science of habit-building, or (finally) floss regularly. Share more below:

To begin with an intentional commitment to this process, read the below statements and sign your name:

I   I am taking good care of myself through habit-building and the transformation of my routines.

II   I am willing to put the principles of habit formation into practice and learn by doing.

III   I will practice self-compassion and embrace failure as I explore what works for me.

Signed By

Date

I   INTRODUCTION:
Your Guide to
The Build-a-Habit Guide

Tomorrow, I'm waking up at 5 a.m. Make that 5:30 a.m. 7:30 a.m.

I'll drink my green juice. Probably.

And no screens after 10 p.m. I mean after midnight. No screens on Saturdays. No screens! Except to log my water intake. Speaking of water intake, have I had my 64 ounces today?

Why can't I get it right?

To exist in the world today is to be made to believe that your life must be a work in progress. We are not living—we are *optimizing.*

   We set daily goals, download the latest tracking app, and swear by our New Year's resolutions, all in pursuit of that one simple "hack" that will unlock the key to perfect skin, the fastest mile, and a fully actualized self.

   This drive for perfection can be insidious (perfection, after all, doesn't exist!), but at its core, it reflects one of our most beautiful human traits: the desire to build a life more aligned with our values. There is nothing wrong with wanting to improve, or desiring routines that provide a greater sense of satisfaction and purpose. The difficulty comes when we believe that this sort of self-improvement can be achieved by bullying ourselves into compliance—often through guilt and shame. Maybe you've set an ambitious goal, and then watched that goal vanish under a mountain of excuses, broken plans, and *"I'll do it tomorrow's."* What once seemed simple, achievable, and *necessary,* is suddenly insurmountable. But building habits doesn't have to be this way.

SUCCESS ≠ WILLPOWER

The implicit message behind this self-improvement vortex is that all you need to achieve lasting change is *willpower*. It's a brute-force, white-knuckle, *"just-do-it!"* approach that prizes self-control above all else. There's something appealing about this oversimplified attitude: *want to go on a run everyday? Just go! Cut out sugar? The only thing stopping you is your own weakness!*

The problem with willpower? It doesn't work.

Study after study reveals that willpower alone is not enough to create meaningful change. One study, for example, tracked the daily lives of individuals who succeed at pursuing long-term goals (i.e. those who are thought of as having "self-control").[1] Researchers found that willpower was consistently unrelated to goal achievement. Individuals who met their goals actually used willpower less often than participants who didn't end up reaching their long-term goals.

So what was the secret formula of these high-achievers? Another set of studies found that people who met long-term goals—consistently meditating, for example, or succeeding in academic pursuits—had stronger daily behaviors.[2] Study participants who succeeded didn't rely on sheer willpower to bully themselves into change. Instead, they leveraged consistent daily actions that they could complete automatically. In other words, they developed *habits*.

What these studies teach us is that if you, like so many others, are struggling to implement your long-term goals, *it is not your fault*. The problem lies in the approach. When we try, over and over again, to strong-arm ourselves into change, believing this time—*this time!*—will be different, we are relying on—or attempting to activate, willpower—a far more fraught, complex, and inefficient tool than we believe it to be. Willpower is just one of many tools in our arsenal, and it is rarely the most effective. Instead, the key to lasting behavior change lies in habit-building.

HOW TO BUILD A HABIT

There's no shortage of buzzy books and blogs about habits full of catchy hooks and secret formulas to success. A simple Google search shows an intimidating laundry list of results on habit-building: "Seven Great Habits of the Most Successful People," "33 Daily Habits of Successful People," or "50 Habits of Successful People You Should Adopt Now!"

Unfortunately, a lot of what pop culture says about habits isn't always evidence-based, rooted in what we know about human nature, or even realistic (after all, we only have 24 hours in a day). For example, the much-repeated idea that cementing a new habit takes 21 days is a myth. That number actually originates from a 1950s self-help book where a plastic surgeon claimed it takes people about 21 days after plastic surgery to get used to their new looks![3] That said, a handful of evidence-based books *do* exist that give an overview of how habits are formed in the real world. While these books can be both informative and enjoyable, they don't guide you through *how* to put principles of habit formation to use. You'll end up with a strong theoretical understanding of habits, but few actual new habits of your own.

This book is different. Yes, we'll show you the research on how to build good habits, but we'll *also* guide you through practical, easy-to-follow activities that let you put those principles to work. We'll pair guidance from experts with actionable tools; lead you through exercises informed by the latest science; and, finally, help you discover how to make meaningful, lasting change. While traditional approaches to behavior change operate with a 'one-size-fits-all' mindset, a much more effective method involves experimenting in order to figure out which strategies work best for you.[4] So we'll do just that—offer experiments that empower you to practice habit-building without pressure, and unlock what helps you to most effectively take action.

THE NEXT FOUR WEEKS

Over the next month, you'll develop the skills necessary for substantive behavior change. This process won't be simple, but it will be informative, valuable, and fun. After all—despite what other books might have you believe—changing your behavior rarely happens in a straight line or overnight. Building daily habits takes time, and—more crucially—experimentation. It's a process that requires patience, play, and a willingness to adjust. That's why this system asks you to be open to make mistakes, tweak as needed, try again, and, above all, to be kind to yourself along the way. This kind of improvisation is necessary in order to figure out what works best *for you*, which is key to making habits stick.

But this work won't end when you turn the last page. The purpose of this guide is not just to help you form a *single* habit, but to teach you the ins and outs of habit-building, so that you can use them again and again throughout your life.

In the next four weeks, we'll guide you through the three steps of our expert-backed habit system:

1   CHOOSE YOUR HABIT:
    Select a key habit to focus on.

2   CREATE A HABIT PLAN:
    Identify the cues you'll use to integrate your new
    habit into your daily life.

3   REPEAT AND REFINE:
    Put your Habit Plan to action and experiment with
    what works (and what doesn't).

But wait, there's more! You'll also:

- Learn the blueprints for habit formation, based on the most cutting-edge scientific research.

- Understand how to apply core habit science principles to your life.

- Master skills such as "habit piggybacking" to leverage your existing habits to build new ones.

- Practice a series of steps to follow when your habit journey seems to veer off-track.

- Get simple and compassionate guidance free of shame, judgment, quick fixes, or scientific jargon.

WHY THIS WORK MATTERS

Let's be clear: this book doesn't hold the key to unlocking some singular version of your most "optimized" self—that person doesn't exist. Part of continual growth is accepting the evolving, unending nature of personal development. What this book *can* do is teach you how to form habits that can help you achieve your meaningful long-term goals. If you've struggled to follow through on past goals, know it isn't your fault. It's likely because you haven't been given the structure, know-how, and support to form the necessary building blocks of behavior change: habits that will stick around even when your motivation wanes.

We can't wait to get started.

II   Understanding Habits

When we think about habits, we often berate ourselves for all we've failed to accomplish, for all the habits we've tried—and failed—to actualize. But the truth is, you already practice hundreds (if not thousands) of good habits each day. From brushing your teeth in the morning to turning off the lights at night, our daily lives consist of small-yet-invaluable habits we perform nearly unconsciously. Without them, we'd struggle to carry out even the simplest of actions. And yet, we often take these habits for granted, if we think about them at all.

Which begs the question: just what exactly is a habit?

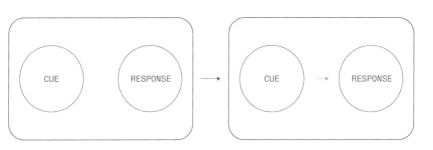

The simple answer? A habit is a shortcut—one that our brain creates when we consistently repeat the same action in the same situation. Think, for example, of how you turn on your coffee machine as soon as you wake up, or lock the door when you leave the house. With repetition, your brain learns to automatically and unconsciously perform these basic responses, providing you with the bandwidth to focus on more difficult or complex tasks.

MAKING A HABIT "CLICK"

Let's consider another example. When you get into a car, you likely buckle up as soon as you settle in. You don't spend time or energy deliberating the pros and cons of wearing a seatbelt—you simply do it, often without even noticing.[5]

Once a habit is formed, it can persist even if you don't act on it every single time.[6] (Forgetting to buckle your seatbelt once doesn't mean you'll never buckle it again). This is great news if you're trying to form desirable long-term habits: even without 100% consistency, your brain can still create a strong mental association for your habit of choice—one that will persist even if you don't execute it perfectly everyday.

Most of the time, we build habits without even thinking about it. To illustrate just how robust the habit mechanism is, consider what can happen after certain brain injuries. Some survivors of brain injuries experience a weakened ability to act in a goal-directed manner, but their ability to act habitually remains entirely intact. In one study, researchers examined patients with severe amnesia who suffered extensive damage to the medial temporal lobe (a part of the brain related to memory) rendering them virtually incapable of retaining information.[7] Within minutes after the amnesia set in, study participants forgot any new experiences.

And yet, when study participants practiced a task that involved selecting one out of two objects—one "correct" and one "incorrect"—they eventually learned to select the "correct" object despite their brains having lost the ability to explicitly retain new information. Interestingly enough, the participants had no conscious recollection of having performed the task in the past, let alone being able to identify the "correct" item. When asked to explain why they chose their selected object, they reported that "it seems to be automatic" and "the hand just goes for it." As this study demonstrates, habits can function independent of conscious thought.

While studies of patients with brain damage may provide an extreme example of habit formation, your own habits are similarly automatic. And these automatic habits are extremely common: one study found that almost half of participants' daily tasks were likely habitual, given that they were performed everyday and in the same context.[8] These habits become so ingrained that—much like buckling up when we get in the car—we don't even need to think about them. This frees up mental space for more difficult tasks, thereby minimizing our daily decision-making burden. In other words, our brains love habits: they give us a break, a cognitive rest, and allow us to devote our mental energy to more complex issues. And that means you can harness the principles that govern habit formation to form the habits *you* want to form.

HOW TO FORM A HABIT:
A THREE-INGREDIENT RECIPE

Three main elements go into forming habits: cues, repetition, and rewards. Let's review each element, using the example of forming a daily vitamin habit to show how all of these factors work together.

Cues

Habits are based on consistent and specific cues. These cues are necessary to habit formation because they signal to your brain that it's time to perform the habit. By crafting clear, carefully-chosen "signals" or cues, you make it easier for your future self to consistently repeat the behavior.

Example: A good way to remember to take your vitamins? Place your vitamins next to the bathroom sink before going to bed. The sight of your vitamins functions as your habit cue.

Repetition

Habits need time and consistency to solidify. The popular "21-day rule" is, in fact, far too short. More recent research suggests that the threshold for habit formation is closer to 10 weeks,[6] and in some cases, could be far higher.[9] This may seem daunting, but an upside is that habit formation doesn't require perfect compliance—daily habits can still form even if you're not wholly consistent.

Example: You've been taking your vitamins everyday for a couple of weeks, so you decide to store your vitamins in the medicine cabinet and assume you'll just remember. *Not so fast!* Most habits don't become entrenched before the 10-week mark. In order for a habit to form, your brain needs long-term repetitive conditioning. On the flip side, if you forget to take your vitamins one day, don't stress—automaticity can still persist as long as you have ample repetition.

Reward

The truth is, humans are not that different from a puppy in training: we respond really well to treats. Rewards signal that an action is worthwhile and should be repeated, but the type and timing of reward matters. You're much more likely to stick to an activity long-term if that activity is *immediately* rewarding.[10-13]

   Why does immediacy matter? You might know that to encourage a puppy to act a certain way, you need to give them a treat right after they perform the desirable action. Give them the treat five minutes later, and they'll have no idea why. It turns out that our brains operate similarly—we just aren't very good at linking delayed rewards to actions that happened long before. To help your brain understand that the reward is a result of the behavior—and therefore that the behavior is worth repeating—make sure that the reward is closely tied to the behavior (or better yet, make the behavior *itself* the reward!).

Example: Let's say your goal with taking vitamins is to "reward" yourself with good health in your old age. This is admirable, but unlikely to motivate in the moment. If, however, you focus on what feels good now—choosing a vitamin that actually tastes good, for example, or pairing the vitamin with a food or beverage you really enjoy—you're much more likely to stick to your habit.

WHAT'S NEXT?

If the science of habits seems dense or abstract, don't worry—we'll help you put all of this into action. For now, all you need to know is that to change, create, or solidify habits, you need to:

- Understand what habits are.

- Understand the key ingredients of habit formation: cues, repetition, and reward.

Armed with this knowledge, creating lasting, meaningful habits is entirely within your grasp. Are you ready to give it a try?

III   Choose Your Habit

This exercise should take you about 5-10 minutes. Find a comfortable spot and, if possible, complete it in one sitting.

Choose one habit to focus on for the next four weeks. Focus on choosing a habit that feels easy, doable, and can be woven into your daily routine. Remember: there's no such thing as choosing the "perfect" habit. You can always go through this process again anytime—this experience serves as your foundation as you learn the skills necessary to form long-term, sustainable habits.

When choosing your habit, follow these three key guidelines:

1   Choose a habit with as few steps as possible that can be
       completed in under 10 minutes.

Why? Simple, easy-to-complete actions more readily turn into habits.[14] That's because the more complex a behavior is, the more difficult it is for your brain to automate it.
       A straightforward, one-step action—like drinking a glass of water when you wake up—might start feeling automatic after only a couple of times.[15] On the other hand, starting an entirely new gym routine will take far more effort and practice to become habitual, and might always require at least some degree of intentional decision making.

2   Choose a habit that you can repeat daily (or every weekday).

Why? Though it's possible to form habits that take place sporadically, most habits require lots of repetition.[16]
       Choosing a daily or near-daily habit will give you the opportunity to repeat your behavior. Repetition can influence habit formation, so select a habit that can be easily repeated.

3   Choose a habit that is meaningful and enjoyable.

Why? When thinking about behavior change, we often imagine it to be about as fun as pulling teeth. Grueling, exhausting habits might be good for us in theory, but they are incredibly difficult to maintain. You're much more likely to stick to an activity that you find immediately rewarding.

The "immediate" part of the reward is key. As we mentioned before, our brains aren't very good at taking delayed reward into account.[12, 13] Choking down celery juice every morning for some imagined health benefit in the future is not a recipe for easy habit formation.

It can be challenging to choose a habit that is both productive and rewarding, but think of this guideline as an opportunity to get creative: try brainstorming ways you can reframe or redesign your habit to be as fun as possible. If your goal is to journal daily, treat yourself to a beautiful new notebook. If you want to build a daily flossing habit, make yourself a flossing playlist with your favorite songs. This strategy—combining an activity that isn't immediately rewarding (such as flossing) with one that is (listening to music)—is called "temptation bundling," and it's a great way to keep yourself on track.[11]

DOS AND DON'TS OF CHOOSING YOUR HABIT:

- Choose a desirable behavior you want to incorporate into your life, not an undesirable behavior you want to avoid. The principles behind breaking a bad habit are very different from those required to build a new one. Even if there is a habit you want to break, focus on a "good" habit to replace it with instead: for example, *"Eating a banana for my afternoon snack instead of a chocolate bar."*

- Choose an action or behavior, not a goal. Lofty goals—such as *"I want to be mindful"*—are aspirational but hard to put into practice. Make sure the habit you choose is a clear action, such as, *"Practice 10 minutes of meditation each morning."*

- Be specific. Very broad goals—such as *"Exercise"*—are difficult to carry out. Instead, think about the specific habit you want to form: for example, *"Complete a 7-minute workout."*

With these guidelines in mind, let's choose your habit.

1   Brainstorm Your Habit

First, make a list of habits you want to form in the near term. No need to rein yourself in; go ahead and dream big! If you need some inspiration, take a look at the activities below. If you've already chosen a habit that fits the guidelines, feel free to skip to Step 3.

PHYSICAL HEALTH	PERSONAL GROWTH	LIFESTYLE	CONNECTION
Take supplements	Do a 10-minute meditation	Make your bed each morning	Do something that would make someone smile
Take medications	Keep a gratitude list of 5 things you appreciate	Drink a cup of water upon waking up	Text a friend
Do a 7-minute workout or stretching practice	Write in a journal	Eat breakfast every weekday	Play with your pet
Floss			
Go for a 10-minute walk outside			

2   Rank Your Options

Take a look at your list. Remember that to set yourself up for success, your habit needs to be:

- Under 10 minutes
- A daily or near-daily activity
- Enjoyable and rewarding

Rank your potential habits based on the above criteria while also considering how important they really are to you.

My Top 3 Habits:

1

2

3

3   Choose Your Habit

Now that you've chosen a habit, write it below. Be as specific as possible by including frequency and duration. Finally, think about why you want to introduce this behavior into your life. This helps you reflect on how this behavior supports your values and long-term goals.

The habit I choose is:

Example: A daily 10-minute meditation.

My habit is important to me because:

Example: Mindfulness meditation is important to me because it will give me more clarity, perspective, and focus. It will also help me de-stress and stay centered even when times get tough.

IV   Create Your Habit Plan

This exercise should take roughly 15-20 minutes. If possible, complete it in one sitting.

Now that you've chosen your habit, it's time to create a Habit Plan. This part of the process is key to building a habit you can stick to long-term. Together, we'll come up with a plan for the actions you'll take before, during, and after you complete your habit. Over the next few weeks, you'll have the opportunity to put this plan into practice and adjust as you learn what does and doesn't work for you.

      The most important principle to keep in mind? *Be specific.* Imagine yourself performing each step of your Habit Plan in detail. When we don't do this kind of detailed planning, we end up deferring decisions to our future self (who will likely defer those decisions to *their* future self!). However, when we drill down to each specific step, we're making behavior change as easy as possible for our future selves: all we'll have to do is act.

      For this next exercise, we use flossing and taking daily vitamins as examples to help you understand the degree of specificity you should aim for. Then, you'll get the chance to create your own.

      Let's get started.

Before

What happens right before you perform your habit? Identify a "before" cue and include the following details:

- *Location:*
  Where does the habit happen?

- *Time of day:*
  When does the habit happen?

- *Preceding Action:*
  What action do you take right before your habit?

Example: In the morning, right after I put on sunscreen, I will go to the kitchen table to take my daily vitamins.

Clear, consistent cues make habits feel automatic and effortless.[15] For example, if you don't have a scheduled exercise time, you end up in a constant state of deliberation. *"Should I go for a run this morning or when I get home from work?"*

Deliberation—a process that requires conscious thought—is the opposite of the automatic nature of strong habits. On the other hand, knowing exactly when and where your habit is performed locks your habit into place.

Additionally, when specifying a preceding action, make sure it's one that is already part of your routine. This is called "habit piggybacking"—harnessing your existing habits to build new ones.[17] For example, you could use your existing tooth brushing habit to build a new flossing habit (*"After I brush my teeth, I will floss"*). Make sure that this is an action you do regularly: if you choose a preceding action that occurs sporadically (*"After I receive a text from a friend, I will take my vitamins"*), cementing your new habit might be a struggle. Your new habit is only as consistent as the cue it relies on.

1   What happens right before you perform your habit?   (Be as specific as possible)

During

Describe in detail all the steps that need to happen for you to successfully perform your habit. Keep in mind that even simple actions can involve quite a few steps. We know this might feel silly, but this level of specificity is key to ensuring the habit becomes routine.

Example: Performance Steps

1   Go to the kitchen table
2   Find Vitamin E and Vitamin D bottles
3   Take out one Vitamin E and one Vitamin D pill
4   Get a glass of water
5   Put vitamins in mouth
6   Swallow vitamins with water

Now that you've articulated all the tiny steps that constitute your new habit, take a few minutes to reflect on what you can do in advance of starting your habit. This prep work means you'll have far fewer barriers when it comes to actually performing your habit.

Ask yourself: what could you do in preparation to set your habit up for success?

Example: Preparation Steps

1   Purchase one to two bottles of Vitamin E and Vitamin D
2   Choose an easily accessible place to consistently put the vitamin bottles
3   Put the vitamin containers on the kitchen counter
4   Prepare a glass of water the night before

2.1   Performance Steps   (Be as specific as possible)

1

2

3

4

5

6

2.2   Preparation Steps: (Be as specific as possible)

1

2

3

4

5

6

After

Now it's time to describe what happens immediately after you perform the habit. This serves as your "habit boundary," a term that describes what happens right after a behavior ends.

Just as you use your *before* cue to signal when to start your behavior, your *after* cue signals the end point. Giving yourself a deadline can be an extremely effective motivator.[18]

Example: In the morning, I sit down and log onto my computer for work after taking my vitamins.

3   What happens right after you perform your habit?   (Be as specific as possible)

Finalize Your Habit Plan

Now that you identified what happens before, during, and after your habit, create a summary of your Habit Plan. This will be your reference as you put your plan into action.

Example:

- Before My Habit I... Put on my sunscreen in the bathroom in the morning.

- During My Habit I... Go to the kitchen counter and take one Vitamin D and one Vitamin E pill.

- After My Habit I... Log on to my computer and start my work day.

4   My Habit Plan for Week I   (Briefly Summarize)

Before My Habit I...

. . . .

. . . .

. . . .

During My Habit I...

. . . .

. . . .

. . . .

After My Habit I...

. . . .

. . . .

. . . .

V   Repeat and Refine

This section walks you through your daily and weekly habit check-ins.
It should take roughly 10 minutes to read and complete.

THE GROUND RULES

Now that you've created your Habit Plan, it's time to put it into
practice. As you work towards your goal, you'll have two types of
exercises to keep you on track:

1   Daily check-in
2   Weekly check-in

These exercises are essential to aligning your life with the habits
you want to adopt. For the next few weeks, you'll experiment
with your plan to see what works and what doesn't, so you can
adjust accordingly.
     We'll ask you to check in everyday for the next four weeks.
At the end of each week, you'll have an opportunity to take stock,
reflect, and adjust your Habit Plan based on what you've learned.

DO I *REALLY* NEED TO CHECK IN EVERYDAY?

It's possible that your Habit Plan is already perfect for you. If so,
tell us your secret! Chances are, however, your plan will need
some tweaking. Maybe you initially hoped to sneak in your
7-minute workout on your lunch break, but after a few days you
realize you're more energized in the mornings. Perhaps you
planned to meditate right after waking up, but soon realized
meditating after breakfast (when you're less groggy) might make
more sense. When embarking on a new habit, it can be difficult to
predict in advance what works and what doesn't. The only way to
really figure it out is to experiment. By taking the time each day
to check in and play with your routine, you'll have a week of data
that can better inform your plan going forward.

OVERCOMING TINY OBSTACLES

No matter how prepared we *think* we might be to take on a new
task, we often overlook the details that enable us to actually
follow through.[19] You can't find your running shoes, or it's too

hot outside, or you didn't set your alarm last night are all great excuses to skip that morning walk. *Not so fast.*

Our natural tendency is usually to believe that these tiny barriers are insignificant. We might underestimate how they prevent us from completing a task. After all, if you're *really* committed, nothing can stand in your way! Right? Sadly, no. When we encounter obstacles, our brains experience a moment of conflict. You're experiencing two contradictory desires—for example, *"I want to go for a walk,"* and *"It's hot and I don't want to get sweaty."*

Internal motivation—or willpower—can sometimes find a way to overcome these obstacles. But motivation is not an endless well, and it waxes and wanes over weeks, days, and even hours.[20] When motivation is running low, we usually default to the easiest option: doing nothing at all.[21, 22] With time, as your daily behavior transforms into a full-fledged habit, acting on your habit becomes the implicit, effortless choice. But to reach that stage, you first need to reflect on the tiny conflicts that you encounter in your daily life, and consider how to solve them.

Exactly *how* you solve each conflict is up to you. If it's hot outside, you might decide to walk in a shady park. Alternatively, you might decide to head out in the evening instead of on your lunch break. Or you might simply decide that heat isn't an excuse, and you'll tough it out regardless (but try not to rely *too much* on this *"just do it"* mentality; as we've learned, you can't rely on willpower when you're tired, busy, or distracted). The specific solution you choose matters less than what you've learned about how you'll navigate these obstacles in the future.

In each daily check-in, make note of any barriers you encountered, and a potential tweak to address that barrier. There's no need to change your entire plan just yet. Not even the best laid plan will work 100% of the time, so you'll want to try out your Habit Plan for at least a week before deciding if and how to change course. Finally, remember that the goal is not perfection. These check-ins are not meant to be an indication of your performance as much as a safe space to find insight and encouragement along your habit journey.

1.1   Before you begin, commit to a consistent time you'll complete this
       guide's daily and weekly check-in. Choose a context that comes *after*
       you do your new habit, and one that works with your daily routine.

       ☐ Right after I perform my habit

       ☐ Right before I go to bed

       ☐ Other (write your own)

       . . . .
       . . . .

       Pro tip: If you already have fixed daily habits (like journaling,
       nightly reading, etc.), create a "habit piggyback" for this daily
       and weekly check-in.

1.2   Now that you've chosen a time, make sure to leave this notebook and
       a pen somewhere that is easy to reach when it's time to check-in.
       For example, if you plan to complete the check-in before sleep, you
       can leave the notebook and pen next to your bed. You can even set
       an alarm or add it to your calendar. Try anything that will help you
       remember to complete your check-in.

Daily Check-In Instructions and Sample Entry

1   Did you complete your habit today?

☑ Yes, I Did   ☐ No, I Didn't

2   How do you feel about having completed (or not completed) your habit today?

Remember, this is a shame-free zone! Think of this as simply an opportunity to

quickly reflect on how the experience was for you.

Example: After my morning walk, I felt refreshed and ready to tackle the day.

3   What was one obstacle you encountered?

Research shows that it's often the smallest barriers that derail us.[23] Jot down one

challenge you noticed. If the habit was very easy for you to complete, you can skip

this question.

Example: I couldn't remember where I put my water bottle and almost gave up

on my walk.

4   What is one small task you could complete now to address that obstacle and
make it easier for you to perform your habit tomorrow?

Brainstorm a practical solution you can commit to for the next day that addresses

your obstacle. If you did not feel that you encountered any obstacles, you can skip

this question.

Example: Fill up my water bottle every morning and leave it by the door.

5   Additional Notes

This is an optional space for you to reflect on the Note From Our Experts below

or to write down anything that came up during the daily check-in. Capturing your

feelings and any challenges you came across can help you learn more about your

motivations, struggles, and goals.

NOTE FROM OUR EXPERTS

We'll provide a new prompt from a behavioral scientist and our
team of therapists to reflect, inspire, and give you more ideas to
consider as you form your habit.

WEEK I:
Daily Check-In Entries

1   Did you complete your habit today?

☐ Yes, I Did   ☐ No, I Didn't

2   How do you feel about having completed (or not completed) your habit today?

3   What was one obstacle you encountered?

4   What is one small task you could complete now to address that obstacle and
      make it easier for you to perform your habit tomorrow?

5   Additional Notes

NOTE FROM OUR EXPERTS

You just took your most important step—the first!

1   Did you complete your habit today?

☐ Yes, I Did   ☐ No, I Didn't

2   How do you feel about having completed (or not completed) your habit today?

3   What was one obstacle you encountered?

4   What is one small task you could complete now to address that obstacle and
     make it easier for you to perform your habit tomorrow?

5   Additional Notes

NOTE FROM OUR EXPERTS

With every repetition, you're cementing
your habit association.

1   Did you complete your habit today?

       ☐ Yes, I Did   ☐ No, I Didn't

2   How do you feel about having completed (or not completed) your habit today?

3   What was one obstacle you encountered?

4   What is one small task you could complete now to address that obstacle and
       make it easier for you to perform your habit tomorrow?

5   Additional Notes

NOTE FROM OUR EXPERTS

It helps to share your habit journey with someone else.
Consider sharing your new habit with a friend and writing about
what the experience of discussing your habit was like.

1   Did you complete your habit today?

☐ Yes, I Did   ☐ No, I Didn't

2   How do you feel about having completed (or not completed) your habit today?

3   What was one obstacle you encountered?

4   What is one small task you could complete now to address that obstacle and
make it easier for you to perform your habit tomorrow?

5   Additional Notes

NOTE FROM OUR EXPERTS

What is one way you could make your habit
more immediately rewarding?

1   Did you complete your habit today?

☐ Yes, I Did   ☐ No, I Didn't

2   How do you feel about having completed (or not completed) your habit today?

3   What was one obstacle you encountered?

4   What is one small task you could complete now to address that obstacle and
     make it easier for you to perform your habit tomorrow?

5   Additional Notes

NOTE FROM OUR EXPERTS

How could you prepare ahead of time to make it easier
for your future self to act on your habit?

1   Did you complete your habit today?

         ☐ Yes, I Did   ☐ No, I Didn't

2   How do you feel about having completed (or not completed) your habit today?

3   What was one obstacle you encountered?

4   What is one small task you could complete now to address that obstacle and
         make it easier for you to perform your habit tomorrow?

5   Additional Notes

NOTE FROM OUR EXPERTS

What's one positive change that your new
habit brings to your life?

1   Did you complete your habit today?

☐ Yes, I Did   ☐ No, I Didn't

2   How do you feel about having completed (or not completed) your habit today?

3   What was one obstacle you encountered?

4   What is one small task you could complete now to address that obstacle and make it easier for you to perform your habit tomorrow?

5   Additional Notes

NOTE FROM OUR EXPERTS

Was there a time this week you found it especially challenging to complete your habit? What went through your mind? What insights or lessons could you learn from the experience?

Synthesis and Reflection
for Week I

You just completed your first week! Time for a victory lap.

By now, you have seven days of experimentation and insights. You might have found this week to be a breeze, and your habit to be smoothly incorporated into your daily schedule. Or, you might have found this week to be a struggle.

Both experiences are equally valuable—as long as you continue to learn what works for you, you're doing everything right.

For now, you'll review your daily check-ins and reflect on your experience. Then, you'll have a chance to revise your plan to address any obstacles you encounter.

After seven days of experimenting, you might decide that the habit you initially chose isn't the best one for your life or routine right now. That's okay! You'll have the opportunity to make adjustments in the next section ("Refine Your Plan for Week II") and recommit to a new habit and plan for next week.

1   How do you feel when you act on your habit?

        I feel refreshed and accomplished when I'm able to go on a walk.
        The fresh air wakes me up and I feel better prepared for my day.

2   Reflect on this past week to identify the most frequent barrier to your habit.

        This can be any obstacle, whether it's your work schedule changing from
        morning to night shifts or not enjoying the taste of your vitamins.

3   Fill out the statement below to identify what you might be coming up
        against when trying to perform your habit:

        I want to:
        Start my day with a walk outdoors.

        But it's difficult because:
        I keep hitting snooze when my alarm goes off.

4   What are two ways you could address and overcome this obstacle?

        (1)   Putting my alarm clock out of reach before I go to bed.

        2   Going to bed half an hour earlier so that I feel more rested.

        Circle whichever solution you think will be the easiest for you to stick
        to, and we'll work on incorporating it into your revised plan.

1   How do you feel when you act on your habit?

2   Reflect on this past week to identify the most frequent barrier to your habit.

3   Fill out the statement below to identify what you might be coming up
     against when trying to perform your habit:

     I want to:

     . . . .

     . . . .

     But it's difficult because:

     . . . .

     . . . .

4   What are two ways you could address and overcome this obstacle?

     1
       . . . .

       . . . .

     2
       . . . .

       . . . .

     Circle whichever solution you think will be the easiest for you to
     stick to, and we'll work on incorporating it into your revised plan.

Refine Your Plan
for Week II

You've reflected on your experience. It's time to take what you've learned and make revisions to your original Habit Plan. If you were able to easily complete your habit everyday, you can skip to the section "My Habit Plan for Week II" and simply rewrite your original Habit Plan.

   If you'd like to change your habit altogether (not just specific parts of the plan), start at question one. If not, skip to question two to revise your plan.

1.1   What is your new habit? Be as specific as possible by including frequency and duration. Keep in mind the habit guidelines from page 27.

1.2   Why did you choose this habit?

Note: If you change your habit, you'll also want to create a new plan.

2.1   Revise your plan to address your most frequent barrier.

       Example: If your habit is to incorporate a daily 10-minute meditation,
       and your most frequent barrier is being interrupted by your
       roommates, it may make sense to change your location cue to a
       different, more private space, or your time of day cue to when you
       know your roommates will be out of the apartment. Alternatively,
       you could add a step in the "During" section: letting your roommates
       know not to interrupt you while you meditate.

2.2   Before My Habit I...

2.3   During My Habit I...

       Performance Steps:

       1

       2

       3

       4

       5

       6

Preparation Steps:

1

2

3

4

5

6

2.4   After My Habit I...

3.0   Briefly describe what happens in each stage of your Habit Plan:

MY HABIT PLAN FOR WEEK II	
BEFORE	
DURING	
AFTER	

WEEK II:
Daily Check-In Entries

1   Did you complete your habit today?

☐ Yes, I Did   ☐ No, I Didn't

2   How do you feel about having completed (or not completed) your habit today?

3   What was one obstacle you encountered?

4   What is one small task you could complete now to address that obstacle and make it easier for you to perform your habit tomorrow?

5   Additional Notes

NOTE FROM OUR EXPERTS

Remember, it's fine if you have to skip some days. As long as you continue your daily practice when you feel able to, your habit will stick.

1   Did you complete your habit today?

☐ Yes, I Did   ☐ No, I Didn't

2   How do you feel about having completed (or not completed) your habit today?

3   What was one obstacle you encountered?

4   What is one small task you could complete now to address that obstacle and make it easier for you to perform your habit tomorrow?

5   Additional Notes

NOTE FROM OUR EXPERTS

As humans, we tend to revert to the easiest choice (say, letting Netflix play the next episode rather than getting up to stretch or move). What are the easy choices in your life? Are these choices helping or hindering you?

1   Did you complete your habit today?

☐ Yes, I Did   ☐ No, I Didn't

2   How do you feel about having completed (or not completed) your habit today?

3   What was one obstacle you encountered?

4   What is one small task you could complete now to address that obstacle and make it easier for you to perform your habit tomorrow?

5   Additional Notes

NOTE FROM OUR EXPERTS

Can you think of an additional reminder (like an alarm or a highly visible sticky note) that you could put in place to cue your habit?

1   Did you complete your habit today?

☐ Yes, I Did   ☐ No, I Didn't

2   How do you feel about having completed (or not completed) your habit today?

3   What was one obstacle you encountered?

4   What is one small task you could complete now to address that obstacle and make it easier for you to perform your habit tomorrow?

5   Additional Notes

NOTE FROM OUR EXPERTS

Tiny barriers matter. Research has found that people recycle more when you put recycling bins right next to them, instead of just a few feet away. What are some barriers to your habit, and how might you remove them to make completing your habit easier on yourself?

1   Did you complete your habit today?

☐ Yes, I Did   ☐ No, I Didn't

2   How do you feel about having completed (or not completed) your habit today?

3   What was one obstacle you encountered?

4   What is one small task you could complete now to address that obstacle and make it easier for you to perform your habit tomorrow?

5   Additional Notes

NOTE FROM OUR EXPERTS

From an early age, we learn to associate what is good for us as tedious or boring. Practice reframing your perception of habit-building. Flossing doesn't have to be a drag so much as a desire. Is it possible to align what you want to do with what you need to do? Or better yet, make what you need to do enjoyable?

1   Did you complete your habit today?

☐ Yes, I Did   ☐ No, I Didn't

2   How do you feel about having completed (or not completed) your habit today?

3   What was one obstacle you encountered?

4   What is one small task you could complete now to address that obstacle and
      make it easier for you to perform your habit tomorrow?

5   Additional Notes

NOTE FROM OUR EXPERTS

In just two weeks' time you've experimented with building a new habit.
It's easy to focus on all the ways that you've fallen short of expectations.
Instead, try listing everything you've learned and accomplished so far.

1   Did you complete your habit today?

☐ Yes, I Did   ☐ No, I Didn't

2   How do you feel about having completed (or not completed) your habit today?

3   What was one obstacle you encountered?

4   What is one small task you could complete now to address that obstacle and make it easier for you to perform your habit tomorrow?

5   Additional Notes

NOTE FROM OUR EXPERTS

Reflect back on how you felt on Day 1.
How does performing your habit feel now in comparison?

Synthesis and Reflection
for Week II

Now that you've completed your second week, it's time to
reflect on how it went, identify the most frequent barrier that
you encountered, and make some adjustments. Refer to the
Expert Guidance on page 56 for help.

1   How do you feel when you act on your habit?

2   Reflect on this past week to identify the most frequent barrier to your habit.

3   Fill out the statement below to identify what you might be coming up
     against when trying to perform your habit:

     I want to:

     But it's difficult because:

4   What are two ways you could address and overcome this obstacle?

     1

     2

     Circle whichever solution you think will be the easiest for you to
     stick to, and we'll work on incorporating it into your revised plan.

Refine Your Plan
for Week III

It's time to take what you've learned and make revisions to last week's Habit Plan. If you were able to easily complete your habit everyday, you can skip to the section "My Habit Plan for Week III" and simply rewrite your previous Habit Plan.

1.1   What is your new habit? Be as specific as possible by including frequency
       and duration. Keep in mind the habit guidelines from page 27.

1.2   Why did you choose this habit?

       Note: If you change your habit, you'll also want to create a new plan.

2.1   Revise your plan to address your most frequent barrier.

        Example: If your habit is to incorporate a daily 10-minute meditation,
        and your most frequent barrier is being interrupted by your
        roommates, it may make sense to change your location cue to a
        different, more private space, or your time of day cue to when you
        know your roommates will be out of the apartment. Alternatively,
        you could add a step in the "During" section: letting your roommates
        know not to interrupt you while you meditate.

2.2   Before My Habit I...

2.3   During My Habit I...

        Performance Steps:

        1

        2

        3

        4

        5

        6

Preparation Steps:

1

2

3

4

5

6

2.4   After My Habit I...

3.0   Briefly describe what happens in each stage of your Habit Plan:

MY HABIT PLAN FOR WEEK III	
BEFORE	
DURING	
AFTER	

WEEK III:
Daily Check-In Entries

1   Did you complete your habit today?

☐ Yes, I Did   ☐ No, I Didn't

2   How do you feel about having completed (or not completed) your habit today?

3   What was one obstacle you encountered?

4   What is one small task you could complete now to address that obstacle and make it easier for you to perform your habit tomorrow?

5   Additional Notes

NOTE FROM OUR EXPERTS

Notice if you tell yourself "It's not a big deal" when you do your habit. Not only is it a big deal (every win counts!), it also means you're starting to normalize the behavior!

1   Did you complete your habit today?

☐ Yes, I Did   ☐ No, I Didn't

2   How do you feel about having completed (or not completed) your habit today?

3   What was one obstacle you encountered?

4   What is one small task you could complete now to address that obstacle and make it easier for you to perform your habit tomorrow?

5   Additional Notes

NOTE FROM OUR EXPERTS

Remember that developing a new habit isn't a battle of willpower, and that doing it—or not doing it—isn't a reflection of who you are.

1   Did you complete your habit today?

☐ Yes, I Did   ☐ No, I Didn't

2   How do you feel about having completed (or not completed) your habit today?

3   What was one obstacle you encountered?

4   What is one small task you could complete now to address that obstacle and
     make it easier for you to perform your habit tomorrow?

5   Additional Notes

NOTE FROM OUR EXPERTS

By now, you may be struggling to maintain momentum.
What is something you could try tomorrow to make your habit more engaging?
(For example, listening to your favorite audiobook on your morning walk).

1   Did you complete your habit today?

☐ Yes, I Did   ☐ No, I Didn't

2   How do you feel about having completed (or not completed) your habit today?

3   What was one obstacle you encountered?

4   What is one small task you could complete now to address that obstacle and
      make it easier for you to perform your habit tomorrow?

5   Additional Notes

NOTE FROM OUR EXPERTS

On days you might be too busy, stressed, or tired to perform your habit, try a
simpler version. For example, stretch instead of a run, or do a quick breathing
exercise instead of a 10-minute meditation. Every step, no matter how small, counts.

1   Did you complete your habit today?

☐ Yes, I Did   ☐ No, I Didn't

2   How do you feel about having completed (or not completed) your habit today?

3   What was one obstacle you encountered?

4   What is one small task you could complete now to address that obstacle and
     make it easier for you to perform your habit tomorrow?

5   Additional Notes

NOTE FROM OUR EXPERTS

If a friend asked you how to build the habit you're focusing on,
what advice would you give them?

1   Did you complete your habit today?

☐ Yes, I Did   ☐ No, I Didn't

2   How do you feel about having completed (or not completed) your habit today?

3   What was one obstacle you encountered?

4   What is one small task you could complete now to address that obstacle and
         make it easier for you to perform your habit tomorrow?

5   Additional Notes

NOTE FROM OUR EXPERTS

The truth is: habits take months to solidify. Stay patient,
keep up the good work, and you'll soon reap the benefits.

1   Did you complete your habit today?

☐ Yes, I Did   ☐ No, I Didn't

2   How do you feel about having completed (or not completed) your habit today?

3   What was one obstacle you encountered?

4   What is one small task you could complete now to address that obstacle and make it easier for you to perform your habit tomorrow?

5   Additional Notes

NOTE FROM OUR EXPERTS

What is something you have noticed about yourself over
the past three weeks? What was most surprising to you?

Synthesis and Reflection
for Week III

Identify the most frequent barrier that you encountered, and make some adjustments. Refer to the Expert Guidance on page 56 for guidance.

1   How do you feel when you act on your habit?

2   Reflect on this past week to identify the most frequent barrier to your habit.

3   Fill out the statement below to identify what you might be coming up
     against when trying to perform your habit:

     I want to:

     But it's difficult because:

4   What are two ways you could address and overcome this obstacle?

     1

     2

     Circle whichever solution you think will be the easiest for you to
     stick to, and we'll work on incorporating it into your revised plan.

Refine Your Plan
for Week IV

It's time to take what you've learned and make revisions to
last week's Habit Plan. If you were able to easily complete your
habit everyday, you can skip to the section "My Habit Plan for
Week IV" and simply rewrite your previous Habit Plan.

1.1   What is your new habit? Be as specific as possible by including frequency
       and duration. Keep in mind the habit guidelines from page 27.

1.2   Why did you choose this habit?

       Note: If you change your habit, you'll also want to create a new plan.

2.1   Revise your plan to address your most frequent barrier.

Example: If your habit is to incorporate a daily 10-minute meditation, and your most frequent barrier is being interrupted by your roommates, it may make sense to change your location cue to a different, more private space, or your time of day cue to when you know your roommates will be out of the apartment. Alternatively, you could add a step in the "During" section: letting your roommates know not to interrupt you while you meditate.

2.2   Before My Habit I...

2.3   During My Habit I...

Performance Steps:

1

2

3

4

5

6

Preparation Steps:

1

2

3

4

5

6

2.4   After My Habit I...

3.0   Briefly describe what happens in each stage of your Habit Plan:

MY HABIT PLAN FOR WEEK IV	
BEFORE	
DURING	
AFTER	

WEEK IV:
Daily Check-In Entries

1   Did you complete your habit today?

☐ Yes, I Did   ☐ No, I Didn't

2   How do you feel about having completed (or not completed) your habit today?

3   What was one obstacle you encountered?

4   What is one small task you could complete now to address that obstacle and make it easier for you to perform your habit tomorrow?

5   Additional Notes

NOTE FROM OUR EXPERTS

"I make sure not to go on my laptop before I complete my habit in the morning. Otherwise, I know I would get pulled in and get distracted."
What can you take away from this tip?

1   Did you complete your habit today?

☐ Yes, I Did   ☐ No, I Didn't

2   How do you feel about having completed (or not completed) your habit today?

3   What was one obstacle you encountered?

4   What is one small task you could complete now to address that obstacle and
       make it easier for you to perform your habit tomorrow?

5   Additional Notes

NOTE FROM OUR EXPERTS

When possible, try acting automatically: sometimes
it's helpful not to ask ourselves if we want to do something
before we start doing it.

1   Did you complete your habit today?

☐ Yes, I Did   ☐ No, I Didn't

2   How do you feel about having completed (or not completed) your habit today?

3   What was one obstacle you encountered?

4   What is one small task you could complete now to address that obstacle and make it easier for you to perform your habit tomorrow?

5   Additional Notes

NOTE FROM OUR EXPERTS

How does your habit reflect an important value of yours?

1   Did you complete your habit today?

☐ Yes, I Did   ☐ No, I Didn't

2   How do you feel about having completed (or not completed) your habit today?

3   What was one obstacle you encountered?

4   What is one small task you could complete now to address that obstacle and make it easier for you to perform your habit tomorrow?

5   Additional Notes

NOTE FROM OUR EXPERTS

What would it look like to stay curious and open
to your new habit formation process?

1   Did you complete your habit today?

☐ Yes, I Did   ☐ No, I Didn't

2   How do you feel about having completed (or not completed) your habit today?

3   What was one obstacle you encountered?

4   What is one small task you could complete now to address that obstacle and
make it easier for you to perform your habit tomorrow?

5   Additional Notes

NOTE FROM OUR EXPERTS

Some small changes end up spreading their positive impact onto other aspects
of life in unexpected ways. For example, going for an evening walk can facilitate
time for phone calls with loved ones. Has your habit impacted anything else in
your life? If so, describe its ripple effect(s).

1   Did you complete your habit today?

☐ Yes, I Did   ☐ No, I Didn't

2   How do you feel about having completed (or not completed) your habit today?

3   What was one obstacle you encountered?

4   What is one small task you could complete now to address that obstacle and make it easier for you to perform your habit tomorrow?

5   Additional Notes

NOTE FROM OUR EXPERTS

What new thoughts and feelings toward your
habit have you been able to notice?

1   Did you complete your habit today?

      ☐ Yes, I Did   ☐ No, I Didn't

2   How do you feel about having completed (or not completed) your habit today?

3   What was one obstacle you encountered?

4   What is one small task you could complete now to address that obstacle and
      make it easier for you to perform your habit tomorrow?

5   Additional Notes

NOTE FROM OUR EXPERTS

Congratulations! You've completed four weeks of repeating
and refining your Habit Plan. How do you feel?

Synthesis and Reflection for Week IV

You've reached the final week of testing, learning, and tweaking your Habit Plan. Reflect on how it went, identify the most frequent barrier that you encountered, and make some adjustments. Refer to the Expert Guidance on page 56 for guidance.

1   How do you feel when you act on your habit?

2   Reflect on this past week to identify the most frequent barrier to your habit.

3   Fill out the statement below to identify what you might be coming up
     against when trying to perform your habit:

     I want to:

     But it's difficult because:

4   What are two ways you could address and overcome this obstacle?

     1

     2

     Circle whichever solution you think will be the easiest for you to
     stick to, and we'll work on incorporating it into your revised plan.

Refine Your Plan for Week V and Beyond

It's time to take what you've learned and make revisions to last week's Habit Plan. If you were able to easily complete your habit everyday, you can skip to the section "My Habit Plan for Week V and Beyond" and simply rewrite your previous Habit Plan.

1.1   What is your new habit? Be as specific as possible by including frequency
       and duration. Keep in mind the habit guidelines from page 27.

1.2   Why did you choose this habit?

       Note: If you change your habit, you'll also want to create a new plan.

2.1   Revise your plan to address your most frequent barrier.

Example: If your habit is to incorporate a daily 10-minute meditation, and your most frequent barrier is being interrupted by your roommates, it may make sense to change your location cue to a different, more private space, or your time of day cue to when you know your roommates will be out of the apartment. Alternatively, you could add a step in the "During" section: letting your roommates know not to interrupt you while you meditate.

2.2   Before My Habit I...

2.3   During My Habit I...

Performance Steps:

1

2

3

4

5

6

Preparation Steps:

1

2

3

4

5

6

2.4   After My Habit I...

3.0   Briefly describe what happens in each stage of your Habit Plan:

MY HABIT PLAN FOR WEEK V AND BEYOND	
BEFORE	
DURING	
AFTER	

Wrap-Up and Reflection

Time to celebrate! You completed four weeks of testing, adjusting, and most importantly, living your Habit Plan. You may have landed on a clear plan on day one, and stuck with it for all four weeks. You may have chosen a new habit halfway through the process. Your habit journey might look very different from what you had initially envisioned. No matter how your experience evolved, you went beyond simply learning about habits and why they are important: you put the principles into practice and took action. In doing so, you gained valuable insights about your motivation and behavior.

So, what's next?

First, a refresher: habits are *automatic, cue-based behaviors* that require little to no conscious thought. The more complex and infrequent a behavior (i.e. working out once a week), the longer it takes for it to become habitual, and even then, these behaviors may still require some degree of conscious thought. Conversely, the simpler and more frequent the behavior, the less time it takes for a habit association to form.

With that in mind, continue to put your simple habit to practice, adjusting and refining as you go. In time, you should find that your habit becomes such an innate part of your daily routine that you barely notice the effort it takes to complete it.

To make sure you're set up for success, here are some final things to keep in mind:

- You may still feel that performing your habit is effortful, and there may be days you simply don't want to do it. That's totally normal! Remember, the average time it takes for a habit to cement is around 10 weeks, but in some cases it can take far longer than that.[6] Every person, habit, and situation is different. Try not to count the days or berate yourself if it's taking longer than you want. Embrace the process, and remember to be patient and kind to yourself.

- You don't need perfect consistency to form a habit. The more repetition you employ, the more your habit becomes immune to those missed days. Give yourself a break if you're having a difficult week—your habit will be waiting for you whenever you're ready to continue.

- Share your Habit Plan and goals with a trusted friend, family member, or coworker, or connect with others pursuing something similar (a mindfulness group, for example). These kinds of informal-yet-public commitments can offer support and help keep you on track.

Remember: this is the beginning of your journey, not the end. We hope you're feeling ready for your next steps. We've included daily tracker entries for you to maintain your progress, and space for you to take stock of how far you've come to celebrate your wins. On the next few pages, you'll also have a chance to reflect on what you've learned so far, and think about what you'd like to take with you moving forward.

1   What's one thing that helped you the most throughout this process?
     Maybe it was involving a friend or adding visual cues.

2   What did you learn about habit formation?

3   What did you find the most surprising about the process?

4   What did you find most challenging?

5   What is one insight that you want to take with you from these four
     weeks, and what is one misconception you want to leave behind?

VI   Daily Tracker Entries

Habit-building is an ongoing process. We've included six weeks of daily entries for you to continue tracking and reflecting. Each entry is designed to take about 1-3 minutes. After the pages are filled in, consider them a record of your progress.

Sunday	M	D	Y

1   Did you complete your habit today?   ☐ Yes, I Did   ☐ No, I Didn't

2   How do you feel about having completed (or not completed) your habit today?

Monday	M	D	Y

1   Did you complete your habit today?   ☐ Yes, I Did   ☐ No, I Didn't

2   How do you feel about having completed (or not completed) your habit today?

Tuesday	M	D	Y

1   Did you complete your habit today?   ☐ Yes, I Did   ☐ No, I Didn't

2   How do you feel about having completed (or not completed) your habit today?

Wednesday	M	D	Y

1   Did you complete your habit today?   ☐ Yes, I Did   ☐ No, I Didn't

2   How do you feel about having completed (or not completed) your habit today?

Thursday	M	D	Y

1   Did you complete your habit today?   ☐ Yes, I Did   ☐ No, I Didn't

2   How do you feel about having completed (or not completed) your habit today?

. . . .

. . . .

Friday	M	D	Y

1   Did you complete your habit today?   ☐ Yes, I Did   ☐ No, I Didn't

2   How do you feel about having completed (or not completed) your habit today?

. . . .

. . . .

Saturday	M	D	Y

1   Did you complete your habit today?   ☐ Yes, I Did   ☐ No, I Didn't

2   How do you feel about having completed (or not completed) your habit today?

. . . .

. . . .

NOTE FROM OUR EXPERTS

Think back to past accomplishments such as graduations, anniversaries,
and promotions. What habits (such as studying, going on dates, and trying
new things) helped you reach these milestones?

Sunday	M	D	Y

1   Did you complete your habit today?   ☐ Yes, I Did   ☐ No, I Didn't

2   How do you feel about having completed (or not completed) your habit today?

Monday	M	D	Y

1   Did you complete your habit today?   ☐ Yes, I Did   ☐ No, I Didn't

2   How do you feel about having completed (or not completed) your habit today?

Tuesday	M	D	Y

1   Did you complete your habit today?   ☐ Yes, I Did   ☐ No, I Didn't

2   How do you feel about having completed (or not completed) your habit today?

Wednesday	M	D	Y

1   Did you complete your habit today?   ☐ Yes, I Did   ☐ No, I Didn't

2   How do you feel about having completed (or not completed) your habit today?

Thursday	M	D	Y

1   Did you complete your habit today?   ☐ Yes, I Did   ☐ No, I Didn't

2   How do you feel about having completed (or not completed) your habit today?

Friday	M	D	Y

1   Did you complete your habit today?   ☐ Yes, I Did   ☐ No, I Didn't

2   How do you feel about having completed (or not completed) your habit today?

Saturday	M	D	Y

1   Did you complete your habit today?   ☐ Yes, I Did   ☐ No, I Didn't

2   How do you feel about having completed (or not completed) your habit today?

NOTE FROM OUR EXPERTS

What's something you can do to recognize
and celebrate a habit-related win?

Sunday	M	D	Y

1   Did you complete your habit today?   □ Yes, I Did   □ No, I Didn't

2   How do you feel about having completed (or not completed) your habit today?

Monday	M	D	Y

1   Did you complete your habit today?   □ Yes, I Did   □ No, I Didn't

2   How do you feel about having completed (or not completed) your habit today?

Tuesday	M	D	Y

1   Did you complete your habit today?   □ Yes, I Did   □ No, I Didn't

2   How do you feel about having completed (or not completed) your habit today?

Wednesday	M	D	Y

1   Did you complete your habit today?   □ Yes, I Did   □ No, I Didn't

2   How do you feel about having completed (or not completed) your habit today?

Thursday		M	D	Y

1   Did you complete your habit today?   ☐ Yes, I Did   ☐ No, I Didn't

2   How do you feel about having completed (or not completed) your habit today?

. . . .

. . . .

Friday		M	D	Y

1   Did you complete your habit today?   ☐ Yes, I Did   ☐ No, I Didn't

2   How do you feel about having completed (or not completed) your habit today?

. . . .

. . . .

Saturday		M	D	Y

1   Did you complete your habit today?   ☐ Yes, I Did   ☐ No, I Didn't

2   How do you feel about having completed (or not completed) your habit today?

. . . .

. . . .

NOTE FROM OUR EXPERTS

Being willing to try and make mistakes is as important, if not
more important, than being able to do something well.

Sunday	M	D	Y

1   Did you complete your habit today?   ☐ Yes, I Did   ☐ No, I Didn't

2   How do you feel about having completed (or not completed) your habit today?

Monday	M	D	Y

1   Did you complete your habit today?   ☐ Yes, I Did   ☐ No, I Didn't

2   How do you feel about having completed (or not completed) your habit today?

Tuesday	M	D	Y

1   Did you complete your habit today?   ☐ Yes, I Did   ☐ No, I Didn't

2   How do you feel about having completed (or not completed) your habit today?

Wednesday	M	D	Y

1   Did you complete your habit today?   ☐ Yes, I Did   ☐ No, I Didn't

2   How do you feel about having completed (or not completed) your habit today?

Thursday	M	D	Y

1   Did you complete your habit today?   □ Yes, I Did   □ No, I Didn't

2   How do you feel about having completed (or not completed) your habit today?

. . . .

. . . .

Friday	M	D	Y

1   Did you complete your habit today?   □ Yes, I Did   □ No, I Didn't

2   How do you feel about having completed (or not completed) your habit today?

. . . .

. . . .

Saturday	M	D	Y

1   Did you complete your habit today?   □ Yes, I Did   □ No, I Didn't

2   How do you feel about having completed (or not completed) your habit today?

. . . .

. . . .

NOTE FROM OUR EXPERTS

Humans tend to revert to default choices. For example, we might only drink
water if we remember to bring our water bottle with us. Default choices aren't
good or bad so much as a reality we can use to our advantage. What are the
default choices in your life? Are these defaults helping or blocking you?

Sunday	M	D	Y

1   Did you complete your habit today?   ☐ Yes, I Did   ☐ No, I Didn't

2   How do you feel about having completed (or not completed) your habit today?

Monday	M	D	Y

1   Did you complete your habit today?   ☐ Yes, I Did   ☐ No, I Didn't

2   How do you feel about having completed (or not completed) your habit today?

Tuesday	M	D	Y

1   Did you complete your habit today?   ☐ Yes, I Did   ☐ No, I Didn't

2   How do you feel about having completed (or not completed) your habit today?

Wednesday	M	D	Y

1   Did you complete your habit today?   ☐ Yes, I Did   ☐ No, I Didn't

2   How do you feel about having completed (or not completed) your habit today?

Thursday	M	D	Y

1   Did you complete your habit today?   ☐ Yes, I Did   ☐ No, I Didn't

2   How do you feel about having completed (or not completed) your habit today?

. . . .

. . . .

Friday	M	D	Y

1   Did you complete your habit today?   ☐ Yes, I Did   ☐ No, I Didn't

2   How do you feel about having completed (or not completed) your habit today?

. . . .

. . . .

Saturday	M	D	Y

1   Did you complete your habit today?   ☐ Yes, I Did   ☐ No, I Didn't

2   How do you feel about having completed (or not completed) your habit today?

. . . .

. . . .

NOTE FROM OUR EXPERTS

It's not just about your habits, but also the habits of the people
in your life. How do the habits of the people around you
influence your behavior?

Sunday	M	D	Y

1   Did you complete your habit today?   ☐ Yes, I Did   ☐ No, I Didn't

2   How do you feel about having completed (or not completed) your habit today?

Monday	M	D	Y

1   Did you complete your habit today?   ☐ Yes, I Did   ☐ No, I Didn't

2   How do you feel about having completed (or not completed) your habit today?

Tuesday	M	D	Y

1   Did you complete your habit today?   ☐ Yes, I Did   ☐ No, I Didn't

2   How do you feel about having completed (or not completed) your habit today?

Wednesday	M	D	Y

1   Did you complete your habit today?   ☐ Yes, I Did   ☐ No, I Didn't

2   How do you feel about having completed (or not completed) your habit today?

Thursday	M	D	Y

1   Did you complete your habit today?   ☐ Yes, I Did   ☐ No, I Didn't

2   How do you feel about having completed (or not completed) your habit today?

. . . .

. . . .

Friday	M	D	Y

1   Did you complete your habit today?   ☐ Yes, I Did   ☐ No, I Didn't

2   How do you feel about having completed (or not completed) your habit today?

. . . .

. . . .

Saturday	M	D	Y

1   Did you complete your habit today?   ☐ Yes, I Did   ☐ No, I Didn't

2   How do you feel about having completed (or not completed) your habit today?

. . . .

. . . .

NOTE FROM OUR EXPERTS

Habits are connected with a sense of happiness and well-being
in life. How does having strong habits make your life better?

Frequently Asked Questions

Q: *Do I have to repeat the exact same habit every single time? For example, do I have to repeat the exact same exercise routine every time to build a physical activity habit?*

A: Building a habit doesn't mean repeating the exact same behavior ad infinitum. Recent research suggests[24] that habitually starting to do something is more important than habitually performing the entire action sequence on autopilot. For instance, if you want to build a habit of doing a 7-minute workout, it's okay if you change up the exercises you perform. In fact, doing so may help you maintain interest over time. But try to keep the beginning of the habit the same (for example, filling up a glass of water and placing your exercise mat on the floor).

Q: *I planned a morning habit but didn't get to act on it. Can I do the habit later on in the day or is it a lost cause?*

A: When planning, the only thing you can be certain of is that things won't go according to plan. When this inevitably happens, it's easy to think that you either follow your plan perfectly, or don't follow it at all. This is what researchers call the *"what the hell"* effect, a common thought pattern where folks may give up if things aren't going 100% according to plan. But when pursuing a long-term goal, it's important to balance the consistency of habit with a healthy dose of flexibility. If you can't do your habit at your planned time, try to complete the habit at a different time. If you find yourself needing to reschedule your habit often, consider how you can adjust your plan to better match the realities of your life, and schedule when you work through the "Repeat and Refine" exercises. Consider this as you work through the "Repeat and Refine" exercises—is there a part of the plan you could tweak to reality-proof it for the next time something happens?

Q: *I was doing my habit consistently until the holidays came around and I completely stopped. How do I restart?*

A: Holidays and vacations are always a tricky time for maintaining habits. Your schedule might fluctuate as you accommodate family visits; you might travel somewhere and miss the familiar cues that usually lead to your habit; or it might just feel like you can't carve out the time to complete your usual routines.

As we say throughout *The Build-a-Habit Guide*, it's completely fine if you miss acting on your habit here and there; but longer disruptions can derail your habit journey if you're not careful. Consider whether there's a simpler version of your habit that you could fit with your holiday schedule. As with your regular habit practice, planning is your friend, so think ahead and plan for how to integrate your habit when your schedule fluctuates during special times of the year.

Even if you end up skipping on your habit for an entire week, that doesn't mean you can't rebound. Additionally, although such disruptions can be impactful early on in the habit formation process, they matter less as your habit solidifies. Once formed, strong habits take a long time for your brain to forget. Ingrained habits can cause some trouble when the habit is something we don't want in our lives. In the case of habits we want, this is great news—even after a longer break, your habit will be there when you restart your habit practice.

Q: *It's week three and I realized I wish I chose a different habit. What do I do?*

A: A core value of *The Build-a-Habit Guide* is understanding that plans change and develop over time. While it might be relatively easy to accept that you need to change things like *where* and *when* your habit takes place, changing the habit itself can feel like you're starting from square one. Remember: you're working toward a lifetime of habits. If you spent two weeks exploring a new workout routine and later realized starting a meditation practice is what you really want, keep in mind that two weeks in a different direction is not much at all when you're working toward a lifetime of habit-building. This learning is a good sign—you're learning what works for you and what doesn't.

Q: *I've been doing my habit consistently for the past four weeks, but it still feels difficult. Am I doing it wrong?*

A: It's normal to feel this way. After you've done something for 20-30 days straight, it feels like you've been checking all of the boxes and you should have already formed an indestructible daily habit. But the truth is, habit formation takes time. Although it's hard to pin down exactly how long—for instance, simple habits take less time to solidify—a good benchmark to aim for is 10 weeks. In the meantime, try to celebrate the wins and observe what you learn along the way. Remember that you are not just building a specific habit; you are learning the lifelong skill of building habits.

References

[1] Milyavskaya, M., & Inzlicht, M. (2017). What's so great about self-control? Examining the importance of effortful self-control and temptation in predicting real-life depletion and goal attainment. Social Psychological and Personality Science, 8(6), 603–611. ▶ https://doi.org/10.1177/1948550616679237

[2] Galla, B. M., & Duckworth, A. L. (2015). More than resisting temptation: Beneficial habits mediate the relationship between self-control and positive life outcomes. Journal of Personality and Social Psychology, 109(3), 508–525. ▶ https://doi.org/10.1037/pspp0000026

[3] Wood, W. (2019). Good habits, bad habits: The science of making positive changes that stick. FSG Press. p. 102.

[4] Klasnja, P., Hekler, E. B., Shiffman, S., Boruvka, A., Almirall, D., Tewari, A., & Murphy, S. A. (2015). Micro-randomized trials: An experimental design for developing just-in-time adaptive interventions. Health Psychology, 34(0), 1220–1228. ▶ https://doi.org/10.1037/hea0000305

[5] Brijs, K., Daniels, S., Brijs, T., & Wets, G. (2011). An experimental approach towards the evaluation of a seat belt campaign with an inside view on the psychology behind seat belt use. Transportation Research Part F: Traffic Psychology and Behaviour, 14(6), 600–613. ▶ https://doi.org/10.1016/j. trf.2011.07.003

[6] Lally, P., Jaarsveld, C. H. M. van, Potts, H. W. W., & Wardle, J. (2010). How are habits formed: Modelling habit formation in the real world. European Journal of Social Psychology, 40(6), 998–1009. ▶ https://doi.org/10.1002/ejsp.674

[7] Bayley, P. J., Frascino, J. C., & Squire, L. R. (2005). Robust habit learning in the absence of awareness and independent of the medial temporal lobe. Nature, 436, 550–553. ▶ https://doi.org/10.1038/nature03857

[8] Wood, W., Quinn, J. M., & Kashy, D. A. (2002). Habits in everyday life: Thought, emotion, and action. Journal of Personality and Social Psychology, 83(6), 1281–1297. ▶ https://doi.org/10.1037//0022-3514.83.6.1281

[9] Buyalskaya, A. (2021). Investigating drivers of repeated behaviors in field data [Doctoral dissertation, California Institute of Technology]. California Institute of Technology Library. ▶ https://thesis.library.caltech.edu/14116/1/ABuyalskaya_Thesis_Final_5%2027%2021.pdf.

[10] Kirgios, E. L., Mandel, G. H., Park, Y., Milkman, K. L., Gromet, D. M., Kay, J. S., & Duckworth, A. L. (2020). Teaching temptation bundling to boost exercise: A field experiment. Organizational Behavior and Human Decision Processes. ▶ https://doi.org/10.1016/j.obhdp.2020.09.003

[11] Milkman, K. L., Minson, J. A., & Volpp, K. G. M. (2014). Holding the hunger games hostage at the gym: An evaluation of temptation bundling. Management Science, 60(2), 283–299. ▶ https://doi.org/10.1287/mnsc.2013.1784

[12] Woolley, K., & Fishbach, A. (2016). For the fun of it: Harnessing immediate rewards to increase persistence in long-term goals. Journal of Consumer Research, 42(6), 952–966. ▶ https://doi.org/10.1093/jcr/ucv098

[13] Woolley, K., & Fishbach, A. (2015). The experience matters more than you think: People value intrinsic incentives more inside than outside an activity. Journal of Personality and Social Psychology, 109(6), 968–982.
▶ http://dx.doi.org.libproxy2.usc.edu/10.1037/pspa0000035

[14] Kaushal, N., & Rhodes, R. E. (2015). Exercise habit formation in new gym members: A longitudinal study. Journal of Behavioral Medicine, 38(4), 652–663.
▶ https://doi.org/10.1007/s10865-015-9640-7

[15] McCloskey, K., & Johnson, B. T. (2019). Habits, quick and easy: Perceived complexity moderates the associations of contextual stability and rewards with behavioral automaticity. Frontiers in Psychology, 10.
▶ https://doi.org/10.3389/fpsyg.2019.01556

[16] Aldrich, J. H., Montgomery, J. M., & Wood, W. (2011). Turnout as a habit. Political Behavior, 33(4), 535–563. ▶ https://doi.org/10.1007/s11109-010-9148-3

[17] Judah, G., Gardner, B., & Aunger, R. (2013). Forming a flossing habit: An exploratory study of the psychological determinants of habit formation. British Journal of Health Psychology, 18(2), 338–353.
▶ https://doi.org/10.1111/j.2044-8287.2012.02086.

[18] Bisin, A., & Hyndman, K. (2018). Present-bias, procrastination and deadlines in a field experiment. NBER Working Paper. ▶ https://doi.org/10.3386/w19874

[19] Kruger, J., & Evans, M. (2004). If you don't want to be late, enumerate: Unpacking reduces the planning fallacy. Journal of Experimental Social Psychology, 40(5), 586–598. ▶ https://doi.org/10.1016/j.jesp.2003.11.001

[20] Rebar, A. L., Elavsky, S., Maher, J. P., Doerksen, S. E., & Conroy, D. E. (2014). Habits predict physical activity on days When intentions are weak. Journal of Sport & Exercise Psychology, 36(2), 157–165. ▶ https://doi.org/10.1123/jsep.2013-0173

[21] Chernev, A., Böckenholt, U., & Goodman, J. (2015). Choice overload: A conceptual review and meta-analysis. Journal of Consumer Psychology, 25(2), 333–358. ▶ https://doi.org/10.1016/j.jcps.2014.08.002

[22] Neal, D. T., Wood, W., & Drolet, A. (2013). How do people adhere to goals when willpower is low? The profits (and pitfalls) of strong habits. Journal of Personality and Social Psychology, 104(6), 959–975. ▶ https://doi.org/10.1037/a0032626

[23] Mazar, A., Tomaino, G., Carmon, Z., & Wood, W. (2022). Americans discount the effect of friction on voter turnout. Proceedings of the National Academy of Sciences, 119(34). ▶ https://doi.org/10.1073/pnas.2206072119

[24] Gardner, B., Phillips, L. A., & Judah, G. (2016). Habitual instigation and habitual execution: Definition, measurement, and effects on behaviour frequency. British Journal of Health Psychology, 21(3), 613–630. ▶ https://doi.org/10.1111/bjhp.12189